To AARON OUR MAN of SCIENCE
and DINOSAUR E[...]
from NANNI and Poppi LINDSAY
who (almost) remember The DINOSAURS
Christmastime 2016 XXXX

*This is
my photo*

My name is

....

The Story of Aaron

First published in 2008

Childnames.net
27 Villarea Park, Glenageary, Co. Dublin, Ireland
info@childnames.net
www.childnames.net
Tel +353 87 936 9888

Written by Eithne Diamond and John Gallagher

Illustrations by Inno Minds
Additional illustrative input by DVD

Further illustrative input,
layout and pre-press: Ferret on the Dartboard

ISBN 978-1-906326-07-4

Design by DVD
Printed in China by Ming Tai Printing Co Ltd

For Conor and Sadhbh
ED and JG

The Story of Aaron

Eithne Diamond and John Gallagher

Illustrations: Inno Minds

Childnames.net

Aaron :

the facts for big people

- The name Aaron is most likely of Hebrew origin.

  - Its precise meaning is unclear but it may signify 'high mountain', 'exalted' or, alternatively, 'brightness.'

  - Another possible source may be the ancient name *Aharon* which is of unknown meaning and probably Egyptian in origin.

    - The name's popularity over recent decades in the English-speaking world is probably due to the legacy of Elvis Aaron Presley.

    - Aaron is the name of a major character in the Bible and, in less detail, in the Koran.

- He lived at a time when the Israelites were slaves in Egypt.

- As the articulate brother of Moses, Aaron attempted to intercede with the Egyptian Pharaoh.

- The Koran records him as being a superior negotiator to Moses; it quotes Moses stating: "My brother Aaron is clearer of speech than I. Send him, therefore, with me as a help."

- According to the Bible, when the Pharaoh fails to relent, a series of nine separate disasters (plagues) befall the Egyptians – including a plague of frogs from the Nile, the basis of our story – finally forcing the Egyptians to release the Israelites from slavery.

- When Moses later spends many days on Mount Sinai talking with God, Aaron buckles to the impatience among the Israelites for new leadership by creating a 'golden calf' from their jewelry.

- Eventually forgiven for this idolatry by God, Aaron becomes the first High Priest of Israel.

- He helps lead the Israelites through the desert, producing water from solid rock with his mitre as evidence of God's continued commitment to their cause.

- Like Moses he is recorded as dying before the Israelites entered the Promised Land of Canaan.

- The main religious references may be found in Exodus 4-14, 5-12, 28:1, 32:1; Numbers 20:23-29 and in the Koran in Suras xx 92, xviii 34 and xix 29.

- A possibly separate Aaron, 'brother of Mary,' is mentioned in the Koran, but this may simply be a descriptive phrase.

- Spelling variations include Arron and Aran. These may be more associated with a placename in Wales and with islands off the coast of Scotland and Ireland.

- *Aaron's Rod* is a yellow flowering plant, referring to the mitre used to draw water from rock in the desert.

- Aaron of Wales was a 4th century saint, who may have been executed.

- Aaron Copeland was an American composer, who won an Oscar for the music of the 1949 movie 'The Heiress.'

- Aaron Spelling was producer of a string of top TV series, including 'Charlie's Angels,' 'Dynasty' and 'Starsky and Hutch.'

- Aaron Lennon has played football in England with Leeds United and Tottenham Hotspur.

Aaron :

the story for little people

O nce there was a boy named Aaron.
He lived with his brothers and
sisters in a very large tent in a land far away.

During daytime they opened the tent
to allow a fresh breeze to cool the air.
At night the tent was closed
to keep the heat inside.

The land in which Aaron lived was ruled by
a very greedy king. The king and his family
did no work at all.

Because Aaron had so many brothers and
sisters the greedy king made them work
very hard indeed.

The king's sons and daughters, brothers and
sisters, aunts and uncles, nephews and nieces
and cats and dogs all insisted on having
cereal with milk and honey for breakfast.

Instead of buying it in the supermarket
they took it from Aaron's family.

Every day the greedy king called Aaron. "You
must work harder, we need more food," he said.
Aaron was very scared.

"I wish the wicked king would leave us alone, but he never will," Aaron said one day while sitting by the pond in his garden.

"I will help you!" said a large frog, who was sitting close to him.

"Tell the king that unless he is nice to you, all my frog friends will come to his next party. We will jump on his table and ruin his food!" the frog said.

The greedy king laughed and laughed when Aaron told him what the frog had said.

" I'm not afraid of silly frogs, even if they can talk!" he giggled, as he munched on his ice cream.

Then he got angry again.

"Just for that you can work for me during your holidays also!" he said.

That night the king was planning a very big party. All of his friends were invited to the biggest and best party of the year.

The table was covered with treats of every type. Chocolate and sweet cake, marzipan and fudge, pineapples and pears, ice cream and crisps, orange juice and lemonade.

At the top of the table, next to where the king sat, there was a big bowl of ice cream. Beside the king's bowl there was not one, but two spoons.
The greedy king wanted to eat his treats twice as fast as everyone else!

He was just about to eat a big bowl of ice cream when he heard a strange noise.

"Croak, croak," came a sound from somewhere under the table.

"What is that?" asked the king.

Then out of the corner of his eye he saw something hop.

"What is that?" asked the king again.

Suddenly the frog and all his frog friends appeared.

They jumped on the table. They knocked over
the chocolate cakes. They put their big,
green feet in the ice-cream.

Then they began to eat the jelly
and cream.

"Stop eating my treats, you
greedy beasts!" cried the king.

"Croak! Croak! Burp!"
said a frog.

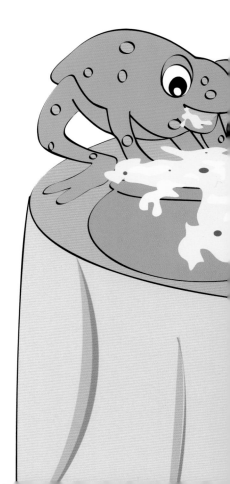

Guess what the frogs did next?

They jumped on the king and licked his face with their long, green tongues!

Yuck!

"Please, please leave me alone! I will do anything you say," the king said.

"Send a text to Aaron," the largest frog said.
"Promise never to be mean to him again."

Aaron laughed when he got a text that said just that.

"C U Never!" he replied.

Then he sent a text to the frogs also. He told them it was OK to leave now.

So it was that Aaron and all his family were free of the wicked king at last.

They lived happily in their tent and they always had enough milk and honey for breakfast each morning. They even had enough food for all their new frog friends.

That is probably why, from that day to this, you will never, never, never meet a frog in any king's palace!

What's in a name?
– more facts for big people

- When actress Betty Joan Perske was given the screen name Lauren Bacall one of the most popular first names for girls of recent decades was created.

- *The name Keira did not exist until the 21st century, except as a misspelling!*

- It is soaring up the baby name charts due to the success of UK-born actress Keira Knightly. She changed the spelling from Kiera to avoid mispronunciation in Hollywood.

- *Today there are thousands of first names. Even the most popular names may account for only 2–3% of the overall total.*

- There were far fewer names in previous centuries. Baptism registers in the UK during the second half of the 16th century record that one in five boys was named William.

- *During the second half of the 18th century, just three names – Elizabeth, Mary and Anne – accounted for 57% of all girls born in the UK.*

- As recently as the early 20th century, some first names were so common in Ireland that a second 'first' name was added for identification, often based on a parent's first name: hence the character Paidín Mike in Synge's famous play 'The Playboy of the Western World.'

- *In the north of England, until the late 19th century, many people relied on multiple names to convey family identity – for instance, Tom o'Dick o'Mary's.*

- Today's parents increasingly use original and inventive first names as a means of conveying identity and 'brand' to their children.

- *Back in the 16th century, however, the Council of Trent ruled that Catholics could name their children only after canonised saints or angels.*

- During the same period, in Britain and USA the Puritans insisted that only names from the Bible were valid. They later allowed names such as Livewell and Safe-on-high.

- *Without any edicts, the double name John Paul suddenly became popular in Ireland after the Pope visited the country in 1979.*

- From the 13th to the 15th century it was common to give the same name to more than one child in a family: the second would be known, for example, as John the younger.

- *The name Jesus is highly popular in Spanish-speaking countries, but considered sacrilegious in much of northern and central Europe.*

- Changing a person's name was once a grave offence. Records in the English city of Rochester state that on Oct 15th, 1515, an Agnes Sharpe 'voluntarily changed the name of her infant son … for which she submitted penance.'

- *Many names still originate from religious history, such as Cate, Katie and Kate from Saint Catherine.*

- How a name is spelled can have religious links also. Sarah is a favourite for Christians, while Sara is preferred by Muslims.

- *The popular boy's name Aaron emerged as a variation of the Biblical Aron, thanks to Elvis Aaron Presley.*

- A name from Irish legend, Conor, has recently become popular internationally but it is often spelled Connor, which denotes a surname in Ireland!

- *Lawrence (Latin), Chloe (Greek literature) and Victoria (history) are examples of other sources for names.*

- Then there's Jack! It seems to have emerged from nowhere – but perhaps from Jankin, a version of John – to become the ubiquitous name of fairy tales and a highly-popular first name.

- *Name 'globalisation' gives us monikers like Tanya, Brooklyn and Chelsea.*

- The general decrease in formality – nobody is now known as Mr, or Mrs, Jones – leads parents to seek ever more imaginative and unique names.

- *Names popular in one country may hardly exist elsewhere. Ever heard of Seren or Cerys? Both are Top 20 names for girls in Wales.*

- Copying celebrities is popular. In 2000 Sonny Sandoval, singer with American group POD, mentioned on MTV that he had named his daughter Nevaeh ('Heaven' backwards). By 2005 more than 3,000 girls were given the name each year in the USA.

- *Finally, before opting for the latest new fab name, it would be both wise and humorous to take a listen to the Johnny Cash song 'A Boy Named Sue.'*

Christening ... Birthdays ... Christmas ...

We'll post your order to you!

Order books from this series
for postal delivery
to **anywhere in the world**.

- **Credit card bookings**:
  click the 'Purchase' link on *www.childnames.net* and follow the steps.

- **Order by post**:
  check the postage costs to your country and the accepted payment methods
  on *www.childnames.net*, then forward the total amount, with the name of
  the book(s) required and your postal address, to:

Childnames.net, **27 Villarea Park**, **Glenageary**, **Co Dublin**, **Ireland**.

A personalised 'My name is ...' poster for your child!

- visit *www.childnames.net*
- click on 'Posters'
- select from a range of illustrations ...
- and follow the links.

Please note:

This service is available by
mail order only (posters are
not available in bookshops).